The Master Is Calling

WORKBOOK

Discovering the Wonders of Spirit-Led Prayer

by

LYNNE HAMMOND

The Master Is Calling Workbook—
Discovering the Wonders of Spirit-Led Prayer
ISBN 1-57399-306-9

© 2006 by Lynne Hammond

Published by Mac Hammond Ministries
P.O. Box 29469
Minneapolis, MN 55429

Table of Contents

A Word to the Reader

If you are reading *The Master Is Calling*, we believe it is because your heart is reaching out to God for closer communion with Him. This workbook is designed to help you cultivate that communion. As you thoughtfully answer the questions it presents, your journey through *The Master Is Calling* will be greatly enhanced. The workbook will help you apply the prayer truths you learn to your own heart and life. As a result, you'll be able to finish this study not only with additional knowledge about prayer, but with an increasingly intimate and powerful relationship with the One who is, even now, calling you to fellowship with Him.

You'll gain the most from this workbook by filling out each section as honestly and thoroughly as possible. Be open and transparent as you realistically assess where you are in your life with Christ today. Carefully consider where you want to be in that relationship in the future. Take time to pray and ask the Holy Spirit to show you what changes you need to make to achieve the progress you desire. Then trust Him to give you the grace to make those changes day by day. As you do that, God will surely lead you into the reality of a deeper life with Him.

In each section of the workbook, you will also be asked to write about the challenges you've encountered in the past that have hindered your fellowship with God. You'll have the opportunity to confront those challenges and ask the Lord to show you how to conquer them.

The Master truly is calling you to walk in higher places of fellowship, faith, discipline, obedience, revelation, and confidence. So at the close of each section of the workbook, you'll be asked to write what you've learned about those divine calls. As you do, be sure to allow the Holy Spirit to speak to you and help you understand exactly what those calls mean to you. Let Him reveal how He wants you to respond to them. And, finally, pour out your heart to God and answer each one of those calls in prayer.

One word of warning. Satan knows that the truths you absorb through *The Master Is Calling* will powerfully and positively affect your spiritual life. So he will undoubtedly try to interrupt or distract you from it. Don't let him do it. Don't allow the enemy and the cares of this world to discourage you or keep you from completing this study.

Instead, press on to lay hold of all God has in store for you, and say with the apostle Paul:

> *[For my determined purpose is] that I may know Him [that I may progressively become more deeply and intimately acquainted with Him, perceiving and recognizing and understanding the wonders of His Person more strongly and more clearly] …*

Philippians 3:10

SECTION 1

The Call to Fellowship

… truly our fellowship is with the Father,
and with His Son Jesus Christ.

1 JOHN 1:3 KJV

Can you imagine the God of all creation being involved in every detail of your life? Can you imagine a day in which every thought, every action, every emotion is directed by the One who knows you best? Can you imagine living in the consciousness of His presence every moment?

The truth is, you can do more than just imagine it. You can believe for it, because the Bible says that's the kind of life God wants us to enjoy—a life of continual fellowship with Him.

Right now, God is calling you to cultivate that fellowship. He is inviting you to develop such an intimate, never-ending relationship with Him that you can confidently say, "I abide in God and God abides in me."

Faith and fellowship with God are inseparable.

This is the journey… This is the call… Walking in daily communion with Him!

MY LIFE TODAY

For I know whom I have believed and am persuaded that He is able to keep what I have committed to him until that Day.

2 Timothy 1:12 NKJ

Paul was able to write this great statement of faith, "I know whom I have believed," because he fellowshipped with God. That fellowship gave Paul an unshakeable confidence in His Word. Wherever you are in your walk with the Lord, He has so much more...

To experience God's presence daily, I:

_____

_____

_____

_____

_____

_____

My time with God is:

_____

_____

_____

_____

_____

_____

MY LIFE AFTER TODAY

And this is eternal life, that they may know You, the only true God, and Jesus Christ whom You have sent.

John 17:3 NKJ

Those times of daily communion, those times of waiting before God and worshipping Him are what bring forth a vibrant prayer life.

To increase my knowledge of the character and nature of God, I will:

Because God said I am the temple of God and that I am a house of prayer, I will:

_____

_____

_____

CONFRONTING THE CHALLENGES

...Did you receive the Spirit by the works of the law, or by the hearing of faith? Are you so foolish? Having begun in the Spirit, are you now being made perfect by the flesh?

Galatians 3:2-3 NKJ

Spiritual debris and emotional junk clutter up your heart!

These are the challenges I encounter that hinder me from experiencing God's presence daily:

_____

_____

_____

_____

_____

_____

Instead of looking to God to fulfill the desires of my heart, I sometimes look to _____ for fulfillment. I realize now, however, that only God Himself can satisfy my need for:

_____

_____

_____

_____

_____

_____

CONQUERING THE CHALLENGES

Now this is the confidence that we have in Him, that if we ask anything according to His will, He hears us. And if we know that He hears us, whatever we ask, we know that we have the petitions that we have asked of Him.

1 John 5:14-15 NKJ

Satan is so frightened of the Christian who abides in God that he will go to great lengths to interfere with those times of fellowship. He will see to it that interruptions, distractions, schedule conflicts arise until it seems almost impossible to find a quiet time and place for prayer.

I place my confidence in God, knowing that He alone is my source and my strength. Beginning today, I will look only to Him to satisfy my need for _____. I will also look to Him for the wisdom and power to overcome those things that have interfered with my times of fellowship with Him. I believe I can begin conquering these challenges by making the following changes in my life and/or prayer times:

_____

_____

_____

_____

_____

_____

_____

_____

_____

_____

UNDERSTANDING THE CALL TO FELLOWSHIP

All who are led by the Spirit of God [not all who are led by each other] *are sons of God.*

Romans 8:14

Did you know you can keep God out of certain areas of your life by refusing to expose them to Him? You can close the door on Him by failing to communicate with Him honestly about them and trying to act like someone you're not.

What is God saying to me about fellowship with Him?

_____

_____

_____

_____

_____

_____

_____

_____

_____

_____

_____

_____

_____

_____

_____

_____

Responding to the Call to Fellowship

Your face, Lord, I will seek.

Psalm 27:8 NIV

*Pouring out your soul
is like cleaning out a cluttered closet.*

What beliefs, attitudes, and behaviors is God asking me to change?

_____

_____

_____

_____

_____

_____

_____

_____

_____

_____

_____

_____

_____

_____

_____

ANSWERING THE CALL TO FELLOWSHIP THROUGH PRAYER

Arise [from your bed], cry out in the night, at the beginning of the watches; pour out your heart like water before the face of the Lord…

Lamentations 2:19

I love them that love me; and those that seek me early shall find me.

Proverbs 8:17 KJV

Seek the Lord. Simply repent. Spend time in His Word and prayer every day.

Keep your soul uncluttered by communicating with the Lord often… honestly… openly… and always straight from the heart.

Follow Him and yield to promptings He puts in your heart!

Dear Heavenly Father,

_____

_____

_____

SECTION 2

The Call to Faith

But without faith it is impossible to please him: for he
that cometh to God must believe that he is, and that he
is a rewarder of them that diligently seek him.

HEBREWS 11:6 KJV

$\mathcal{F}$aith is the most basic, essential ingredient of the Christian life. It took faith for you to receive Jesus as your Lord and Savior, and it takes faith to continue growing in your relationship with Him.

If you think you don't know how to live by faith, think again. You live by faith in natural things every day of your life. You have faith that lights will come on when you flip the light switch. You have faith that the car will start when you turn the key. You have faith that when you insert your ATM card, the machine will give you money (most of the time anyway).

Faith is what connects you to everything in the realm of the Spirit.

But have you developed the "God kind" of faith?
Have you cultivated the kind of faith that empowers you to speak the Word of God with full assurance that what God promised, He is not only able but willing to do?

That's the kind of faith that pleases God. That's the kind of faith that guarantees answers to your prayers. It's the kind of faith Jesus was talking about when He said, "…Whatever things you ask when you pray, believe that you receive them, and you will have them." (Mark 11:24 NKJ)

This is the journey… This is the call… Walking by faith, not by sight!

MY LIFE TODAY...

Therefore, brethren, having boldness to enter the Holiest by the blood of Jesus... let us draw near with a true heart in full assurance of faith, having our hearts sprinkled from an evil conscience and our bodies washed with pure water.

Hebrews 10:19, 22 NKJ

To flow in the Spirit you must release the same kind of faith used for salvation... If you are not releasing faith, you are not going anywhere.

My prayer life reflects my faith because every time I pray, I believe that:

_____

_____

_____

_____

_____

_____

_____

_____

_____

_____

MY LIFE AFTER TODAY...

Faith comes by hearing, and hearing by the word of God.

Romans 10:17 NKJ

Develop your faith to flow in the Holy Spirit by studying and meditating on the promises God has given us about Him.

I will increase and strengthen my faith by reading and meditating on the following scripture passages. (Select your favorites from *The Master Is Calling* book chapters 4-6.):

_____   _____

_____   _____

_____   _____

I will exercise that faith by:

_____

_____

_____

_____

_____

_____

_____

_____

CONFRONTING THE CHALLENGES

*And I will ask the Father, and He will give you another Comforter
(Counselor, Helper, Intercessor, Advocate, Strengthener, and
Standby), that He may remain with you forever—the Spirit
of Truth, Whom the world cannot receive (welcome, take to
its heart), because it does not see Him or know and recognize
Him. But you know and recognize Him, for He lives with you
[constantly] and will be in you.*

John 14:16-17

*If you've had doubts about your ability to
recognize the Holy Spirit, you can put
those doubts out of your mind. Jesus
Himself has given you His Word that
you can do it.*

In the past, I have been hesitant to step out in faith and follow
the promptings of the Holy Spirit in my prayer life because:

_____

_____

_____

_____

_____

_____

_____

_____

_____

_____

_____

_____

_____

CONQUERING THE CHALLENGES

...When He, the Spirit of Truth (the Truth-giving Spirit) comes, He will guide you into all the Truth (the whole, full Truth) For He will not speak His own message [on His own authority]; but He will tell whatever He hears [from the Father; He will give the message that has been given to Him], and He will announce and declare to you the things that are to come [that will happen in the future].

John 16:13

God is big enough to speak to you. I don't care how dense you think you are, God knows exactly how to get His communications through to your heart. He didn't have any trouble speaking to a donkey in the Old Testament (Numbers 22), so He can surely handle you.

19

From now on, I will more confidently expect and boldly follow the leading of the Holy Spirit in my prayer life because:

_____

_____

_____

_____

_____

_____

_____

_____

_____

_____

_____

_____

_____

UNDERSTANDING THE CALL TO FAITH

For as many as are led by the Spirit of God, these are the sons of God.

Romans 8:14 NKJ

In prayer, we always have to travel by faith.
Every kind of prayer requires faith.

I sense the Spirit of God leading me to further develop my faith so I can pray with confidence about the following areas of my life:

_____

_____

_____

_____

_____

_____

_____

_____

_____

_____

_____

_____

_____

_____

_____

_____

RESPONDING TO THE CALL TO FAITH
THROUGH PRAYER

Draw near to God and He will draw near to you.

James 4:8 NKJ

Purpose to make a connection with Him by becoming consciously aware, not just that you are speaking but that you are speaking to Him.

What is God asking me to do to grow in faith?

_____

_____

_____

_____

_____

_____

_____

_____

_____

_____

_____

_____

_____

_____

_____

_____

ANSWERING THE CALL TO FAITH

...I now perceive and understand that God shows no partiality and is no respecter of persons.

Acts 10:34

God wants to reveal Himself to us. It's His nature to do so. He has chosen to hide Himself from those who don't meet the criteria and He has chosen to reveal Himself to those who do.
Faith is the criteria.

Dear Heavenly Father,

_____

_____

_____

_____

_____

_____

_____

_____

_____

_____

_____

_____

_____

_____

_____

_____

_____

_____

_____

_____

_____

_____

_____

_____

_____

_____

_____

_____

_____

_____

_____

_____

Prayer without faith is prayer without power.

SECTION 3

The Call to Discipline

If ye abide in me, and My words abide in you, ye shall
ask what ye will, and it shall be done unto you.

JOHN 15:7 KJV

*I*f the day-to-day discipline of the Christian life is not your favorite subject, you are not alone.

Many, perhaps even the majority of, believers seem to have difficulty mastering the basic, day-to-day requirements of spiritual growth—time in the Word, time in prayer, and learning to sit still long enough to hear the voice of the Lord. But, take heart. It can be done.

What's more, if you are going to become all God has called you to be, it must be done. And God Himself will strengthen you and help you do it.

By His grace, you can develop the discipline it takes to walk in fellowship with the Father. You can become a person of prayer and enjoy a life filled with purpose.

You'll never get anywhere spiritually by going to church once in a while and reading your Bible only on occasion. You need a constant supply of the Word. For it's the Word that is fresh and alive in you today; it's the truth that is proceeding from the mouth of God into your heart right now that will work most powerfully in you.

Jesus separated Himself from friends and family to seek His Father and He is asking you to follow His example. He is calling you to pray as He prayed, to hear the Father the way

He heard the Father, and to speak only what the Father speaks. To answer that call, you must make a daily decision to put Him first in your life. You must embrace discipline as an act of your will.

This is the journey... This is the call... Living a disciplined life!

MY LIFE TODAY...

Let the word of Christ dwell in you richly in all wisdom, teaching and admonishing one another in psalms and hymns and spiritual songs, singing with grace in your hearts to the Lord.

Colossians 3:16 NKJ

It takes time for us to cultivate a relationship with Him, not just time spent talking either, but time spent in quiet waiting.

A balanced devotional life includes: (1) reading and meditating the Word of God; (2) worshipping and praising the Lord; (3) speaking to and making requests of the Lord; and (4) waiting on the Lord to receive direction and to hear His voice. I would describe those four areas of my devotional life as follows:

_____

_____

_____

_____

_____

MY LIFE AFTER TODAY...

My son, give attention to my words. Incline your ear to my sayings. Do not let them depart from your eyes. Keep them in the midst of your heart.

Proverbs 4:20-21 NKJ

People who feed their spirits constantly with the Word of God can more easily follow their hearts. I believe that's because their hearts have grown so strong that it exerts a greater pull than the flesh does.

In order to strengthen my heart, I will give more attention to the Word of God. I will do this by making the following changes or additions to my devotional life:

_____

_____

_____

_____

_____

_____

_____

_____

_____

CONFRONTING THE CHALLENGES

But those who wait on the Lord shall renew their strength;
they shall mount up with wings like eagles, they shall run and
not be weary, they shall walk and not faint.

Isaiah 40:31 NKJ

What a blessing it is to exchange our limited,
human strength for the unlimited strength
of God Himself! Yet many times we pass
up that blessing because we don't
take the time to wait.

**These are the hindrances that keep me from waiting on the Lord
until I receive the direction and strength I need from Him:**

_____

_____

_____

_____

_____

_____

_____

_____

_____

_____

_____

_____

CONQUERING THE CHALLENGES

Wait on the Lord; Be of good courage, And He shall strengthen your heart; Wait, I say, on the Lord.

Psalm 27:14 NKJ

Waiting on the Lord doesn't necessarily require hours of your time, and it doesn't always have to be done just in your prayer closet. If you'll ask the Lord to help you, you can learn to wait on Him at the office during a break time, when you're driving your car, at a restaurant while you're waiting for your food—anywhere!

This is what God is asking me to do to increase my capacity to wait on Him:

_____

_____

_____

_____

_____

_____

_____

_____

UNDERSTANDING THE CALL TO DISCIPLINE

*Look carefully then how you walk! Live purposefully and
worthily and accurately...*

Ephesians 5:15

*It takes great grace, great discipline, and great
desire to come to a place where we can
consistently hear God's voice. This is
the highest challenge of the
Christian life.*

What is required to live a powerful life of prayer?

_____

_____

_____

_____

_____

_____

_____

_____

_____

_____

_____

_____

_____

_____

_____

_____

RESPONDING TO THE CALL TO DISCIPLINE

But be doers of the word, and not hearers only, deceiving yourselves.

James 1:22 NKJ

Jesus said each one of us is a house of prayer and in every orderly house, there are rules of conduct that set the tone. There are certain habits that help the household run smoothly. The same is true in your house of prayer. Even though prayer itself is a matter of the heart, there are a few prayer habits you can adopt that will benefit you greatly.

I believe God is asking me to make the following prayer habits a regular part of my life:

_____

_____

_____

_____

_____

_____

_____

_____

_____

_____

ANSWERING THE CALL TO DISCIPLINE THROUGH PRAYER

My grace is sufficient for you, for My strength is made perfect in your weakness.

2 Corinthians 12:9 NKJ

Sometimes God doesn't want us to do; He just wants us to...

Be comfortable in His presence

Set our hearts on Him

Be aware of our desperate need for Him

Be aware of His promise to fill that need to overflowing.

Dear Heavenly Father,

_____

_____

_____

_____

_____

_____

_____

_____

SECTION 4

The Call to Obedience

…Now we serve not under [obedience to] the old code of written regulations, but [under obedience to the promptings] of the Spirit in newness of life.

ROMANS 7:6

*W*hat does it mean to obey God? Does it mean you must abide by scriptural laws like the Israelites did in the Old Testament? Does it mean you must keep countless religious rules and regulations?

No, thank God, it doesn't.

As New Testament believers, we don't have to live our lives "by the law" anymore. We have the joy of living in obedience to the promptings of the Holy Spirit within us. We can boldly follow the leading of our hearts because God Himself has written His laws within us (Hebrews 8:10). He has moved into us and made us His home! (John 14:23)

That's why we don't have to depend on written lists or follow predetermined formulas when we pray. We have the Holy Spirit Himself to guide us. He is the greatest teacher and intercessor of all. He knows far better than we do what we need to pray for and how we can most effectively offer those prayers.

We must realize we can't afford to be directed by outward appearances and opinions. We must be led by the Holy Spirit. He knows where our prayers are truly needed.

But He can't help us if we don't pay attention to Him. He needs us to seek and obey His leadership. Instead of rushing ahead and praying our own prayers our own way, we must stop... look for His help... and listen to His voice. Then we must respond in obedience to Him.

On the other side of that obedience is a prayer life so powerful, so accurate, and so effective that it will satisfy the deepest desires of our hearts. For when we obey the Holy Spirit in prayer, God is able to do exceedingly abundantly above all that we can ask or think.

This is the journey... This is the call... Walking in obedience!

My Life Today...

Likewise the Spirit also helps in our weaknesses. For we do not know what we should pray for as we ought, but the Spirit Himself makes intercession for us with groanings which cannot be uttered.

Romans 8:26 NKJ

As you follow the promptings of the Holy Spirit in your prayer life and allow Him to be your guide, you will not always be praying about those things that seem to your natural mind to be most in need of prayer.

People's prayer lives can be directed by need, by intellectual reasoning, by what they've been taught to pray for, or by the leadership and inspiration of the Holy Spirit. My prayer life is primarily directed by:

_____

_____

_____

_____

_____

_____

_____

MY LIFE AFTER TODAY...

"For My thoughts are not your thoughts, nor are your ways My ways," says the Lord. "For as the heavens are higher than the earth, so are My ways higher than your ways, and My thoughts than your thoughts."

Isaiah 55:8-9 NKJ

True prayer never starts with us. It always starts with God. It is a cycle that begins when He puts His thoughts and ways into our hearts.

Now that I am more conscious of the fact that true prayer starts with God, when I pray I will:

41

_____

_____

_____

_____

_____

_____

_____

CONFRONTING THE CHALLENGES

Seek the Lord while He may be found, Call upon Him while He is near.

Isaiah 55:6 NKJ

In your life of prayer, there will also be times when instead of jumping on the bandwagon of busyness, the Spirit will lead you to be still and pray. Many people (not just heathens, but good, God-loving Christians) won't understand. But you must determine in advance that no matter what others may say and do, you are going to follow the Word of God and unction of the Holy Spirit.

In the past, I have not always obeyed God when He prompted me to pray because:

_____

_____

_____

_____

_____

_____

_____

_____

_____

CONQUERING THE CHALLENGES

Pray without ceasing.

1 Thessalonians 5:17 NKJ

The Holy Spirit is living inside you. And He isn't
just sitting around in there; He's at work. He is
there to empower us to "pray without ceasing."
As we go about the daily affairs of
our lives, we can yield ourselves to the Holy
Spirit. We can listen to our hearts, catch
our cues, and lift them up to
the Lord in prayer.

43

Because I desire to obey God in prayer, in the future I will:

_____

_____

_____

_____

_____

_____

_____

_____

_____

UNDERSTANDING THE CALL TO OBEDIENCE

...He Who sent Me is true (reliable), and I tell the world [only] the things that I have heard from Him... I tell the things which I have seen and learned at My Father's side...

John 8:26, 38

Jesus followed the leadership of the Holy Spirit by seeing and hearing... When He spoke of seeing and hearing, He was referring to that which is done in the realm of the Spirit.

He was never directed by His flesh.

44

Why is it so important for me to hear God speak every day?

_____

_____

_____

_____

_____

_____

_____

_____

_____

_____

_____

RESPONDING TO THE CALL TO OBEDIENCE

For it is God who works in you both to will and to do for His good pleasure.

Philippians 2:13 NKJ

Only by discerning the direction of the Holy Spirit can we truly pray as we ought. It is essential for us to clearly understand how to follow His leadership.

I will further cultivate my sensitivity to the leadership of the Holy Spirit and develop my ability to discern God's voice by:

ANSWERING THE CALL TO OBEDIENCE THROUGH PRAYER

He who supplies you with His marvelous [Holy] Spirit and works powerfully and miraculously among you... because of your believing...

Galatians 3:5

Remember, God is the One who said He would speak to you and show you things by the Holy Spirit. It's His responsibility to get the job done. He is big enough to do it, too. So just trust Him. Believe Him to do whatever it takes to get His message through to you. Don't get tied up in knots of apprehension trying to see and hear. Relax and let the Spirit do His work in you.

Dear Heavenly Father,

_____

_____

_____

_____

_____

_____

_____

_____

SECTION 5

The Call to Revelation

But as it is written, Eye hath not seen, nor ear heard,
neither have entered into the heart of man, the things
which God hath prepared for them that love Him. But
God hath revealed them unto us by His Spirit.

1 CORINTHIANS 2:9-10 KJV

I *know something you don't know.* Most all of us, at one time or another, have said those words. They're an open invitation, meant to inspire others to ask, to seek, and to press us to reveal the secret we're so joyfully hiding.

Amazing as it may seem, God is saying those very same words to you, as a believer. He wants you to know His Word is full of mysteries, not hidden from you, but hidden for you. He's inviting you to ask and keep asking, to seek and keep seeking, to knock and keep knocking… until those mysteries are revealed.

The Word of God reveals that since the beginning, when God gave man dominion over the earth, He has worked in a partnership with men and women of faith and prayer.

Sadly, many believers never accept God's invitation because they're afraid they'll ask and seek in vain. They worry that, despite their best efforts, God will just keep hiding… and hiding… and hiding Himself from them.

But those fears are unfounded. God has already promised to reward all those who diligently seek Him—and that promise includes you. He wants you to know Him. He wants to reveal His nature, His character, and His love to you. He wants you to know His ways. He wants you to leave earth's limited perspective and let the Holy Spirit lead you into supernatural places with Him. He is calling you to a new place in prayer where you will partner with Him as He shows you things to come.

This is the journey... This is the call... Living in revelation!

MY LIFE TODAY...

He who speaks in a tongue edifies himself.

1 Corinthians 14:4 NKJ

But you, beloved, building yourselves up on your most holy faith, praying in the Holy Spirit.

Jude 20 NKJ

It takes strength to walk with God.

I need to build myself up and strengthen myself in the Lord so that I can accomplish more and enjoy greater victory in the following areas of my life:

_____

_____

_____

_____

_____

_____

_____

_____

_____

_____

_____

_____

MY LIFE AFTER TODAY...

For he who speaks in a tongue does not speak to men but to God, for no one understands him; however, in the spirit he speaks mysteries.

1 Corinthians 14:2 NKJ

Be willing to start at the beginning and be willing to grow in this gift that only God can give.

Set goals and stretch past your comfort zone.

I will edify myself and grow stronger in prayer by:

_____

_____

_____

_____

_____

_____

_____

_____

CONFRONTING THE CHALLENGES

I will pray with the spirit, and I will also pray with the understanding...

1 Corinthians 14:15 NKJ

For tongues to be the genuine form of communication God designed them to be, we must have our hearts and minds hooked up to Him.

These are some thoughts that sometimes hinder me from praying as freely or as often as I'd like to in tongues:

_____

_____

_____

_____

_____

_____

_____

_____

_____

_____

_____

CONQUERING THE CHALLENGES

Likewise the Spirit also helps in our weaknesses. For we do not know what we should pray for as we ought, but the Spirit Himself makes intercession for us with groanings which cannot be uttered.

Romans 8:26 NKJ

Just keep your focus on God. Purpose to express your love and gratitude to Him and enjoy the wonderful gift of tongues.

The Holy Spirit is an intercessor. He cannot pray unless we pray. He is dependent on us just as we are dependent on Him.

The Lord is leading me to press through the thoughts that have tried to hinder me from praying in tongues by making the following changes:

_____

_____

_____

_____

_____

_____

_____

_____

_____

_____

_____

UNDERSTANDING THE CALL TO REVELATION

Yet to us God has unveiled and revealed them by and through His Spirit, for the (Holy) Spirit searches diligently, exploring and examining everything, even sounding the profound and bottomless things of God.

1 Corinthians 2:10

Just imagine: Every answer you'll ever need to know, the whole of God's divine counsel, all His plans for the future—everything— is inside you right now.

56

God planned a course especially for you before you were born. Pray out those mysteries. Purpose to reach down into your heart and hook into them.

When I pray in tongues and ask God to reveal the things I need to know to fulfill His plan for my life, I can be confident He will do it because:

_____

_____

_____

_____

_____

_____

_____

_____

_____

_____

_____

_____

_____

_____

_____

_____

_____

RESPONDING TO THE CALL TO REVELATION

A voice of one who cries: Prepare in the wilderness the way of the Lord [clear away the obstacles]; make straight and smooth in the desert a highway for our God!

Isaiah 40:3

By speaking the inspired words of God by the anointing of the Holy Spirit, we clear a highway for our God; we clear a path in the realms of the Spirit so He can move and walk.

What is God asking me to do so that He can more fully reveal Himself and His plans to me?

_____

_____

_____

_____

_____

_____

_____

_____

_____

_____

ANSWERING THE CALL TO REVELATION THROUGH PRAYER

Call to Me and I will answer you and show you great and mighty things, which you do not know.

Jeremiah 33:3 NKJ

The Holy Spirit wants to take us higher. He wants to take us on marvelous adventures in prayer and show us the great plans and realm of God.

Let us learn from Jesus' example. Let us follow Him, leave earth's limited perspective behind, and let the same Holy Spirit who led Him, lead us into those supernatural places. Let us fall on our knees in faith and cry "Lord, help us pray."

Dear Heavenly Father,

_____

_____

_____

_____

_____

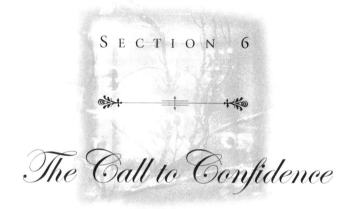

SECTION 6

The Call to Confidence

Do not, therefore, fling away your fearless confidence, for it carries a great and glorious compensation of reward.

HEBREWS 10:35-36

Now this is the confidence that we have in Him, that if we ask anything according to His will, He hears us. And if we know that He hears us, whatever we ask, we know that we have the petitions that we have asked of Him.

1 JOHN 5:14-15 NKJ

*T*here is a smile, a look, a feeling that comes over you when you know God has heard your prayers. There's a boldness, a sense of calm assurance that comes when you're confident that He has granted your request. Joy bubbles up within you and, despite all natural evidence to the contrary, you know that you know God will be faithful to do what He has promised. You know that you know that everything will be all right!

That kind of confidence doesn't always come the first time we pray. But if we'll continue to persevere, if we'll continue to search the Word and seek the face of God, He'll help us get so settled upon His promises that nothing can shake us. He'll give us the strength to stand and rejoice over every situation until we see the salvation of the Lord.

Every time you pray you must believe your prayer changed things in the realm of the spirit even if you cannot yet see evidence of those changes in the natural world.

He will fill us with confidence, not in ourselves, but in the One who cannot lie.

This is the journey... This is the call... Walking in confidence in Him!

MY LIFE TODAY...

Also [Jesus] told them a parable to the effect that they ought always to pray and not to turn coward (faint, lose heart, and give up)...

Luke 18:1

To persevere means to see something all the way through to the end. It means once God puts a person or a situation in your heart, you stay with it. It may appear that the more you pray, the worse the situation becomes. But, even so, you refuse to give up until God's will is done.

When my prayer is not answered immediately, I:

_____

_____

_____

_____

_____

_____

_____

_____

_____

MY LIFE AFTER TODAY...

Put Me in remembrance; Let us contend together, state your case, that you may be acquitted.

Isaiah 43:26 NKJ

You must know what the Bible promises you. You must see a clear inner image of that promise being fulfilled.

Plead your case. Base your case on promises and precedent from the Bible!

To experience greater confidence, when I pray, I will:

_____

_____

_____

_____

_____

_____

_____

_____

_____

Confronting the Challenges

And there is no one who calls on Your name, who stirs himself up to take hold of You.

Isaiah 64:7 NKJ

Meditate on the Word until it becomes bigger in your heart than any situation—bigger than any doubt Satan can bring.

What circumstances/people/things have I allowed to shake my confidence in the Word?

_____

_____

_____

_____

_____

_____

_____

_____

_____

_____

_____

_____

_____

_____

_____

CONQUERING THE CHALLENGES

...Let your heart retain my words; Keep my commands, and live. Get wisdom! Get understanding! Do not forget, nor turn away from the words of my mouth.

Proverbs 4:4-5 NKJ

The way you act, speak, and pray will be determined by where you are looking. If you're looking at the Word, you'll be filled with faith.

Settle down on the promise; focus the eyes of your heart on what God has promised.

I will increase my ability to persevere in prayer by making the following changes:

_____

_____

_____

_____

_____

_____

_____

_____

_____

UNDERSTANDING THE CALL TO CONFIDENCE

... the love of God has been poured out in our hearts by the Holy Spirit who was given to us.

Romans 5:5 NKJ

Love will move you to pray. If you yield to the love of God within you, it will be a compelling force in your life.

What does God promise about a life filled with confidence in His love?

_____

_____

_____

_____

_____

_____

_____

_____

_____

_____

_____

_____

_____

_____

_____

RESPONDING TO THE CALL TO CONFIDENCE

This is My commandment, that you love one another as I have loved you. Greater love has no one than this, than to lay down one's life for his friends.

John 15:12-13 NKJ

God delights in mercy. He is always looking for a way to preserve people and deliver them. All He needs is one person who will pray!

What is God speaking to my heart about loving Him and others more fully?

_____

_____

_____

_____

_____

_____

_____

_____

_____

_____

_____

_____

_____

ANSWERING THE CALL TO CONFIDENCE
THROUGH PRAYER

Love never fails.

1 Corinthians 13:8 NKJ

Your job in prayer is to hold God's Word before
Him and keep it there until that Word is
manifested in the person or situation
for which you are praying.

...God's love in you will get you started in prayer.
It will keep you safely conducting
prayer's power and it will give you
the divine energy to pray all the way
through to victory.

Dear Heavenly Father,

_____

_____

_____

_____

_____

_____

_____

_____

_____

_____

_____

_____

_____

_____

_____

_____

_____

_____

Prayer doesn't qualify us as 'super saints'...
Prayer is basic Christianity!

CULTIVATE A LIFE OF PRAYER

Lifestyle of prayer...

It takes time for God to develop you in it.

Just get started.

Teach yourself to walk
with a consciousness of God.

Listen to your heart throughout the day.

Study and meditate what the Bible says
about the work of the Holy Spirit.

... The measure [of thought and study] you give [to the truth you hear] will be the measure [of virtue and knowledge] that comes back to you ...

Mark 4:24

For on that day when you stand before Jesus and He reveals the miracles that were brought through your prayers, you'll be ever so grateful that amidst the clamoring needs and distractions of life you chose to follow Him.

Prayer of Salvation

A born again, committed relationship with God is the key to a victorious life. Jesus, the Son of God, laid down His life and rose again so that we could spend eternity with Him in heaven and experience His absolute best on earth. The Bible says, "For God so loved the world, that he gave his only begotten Son, that whosoever believeth in him should not perish, but have everlasting life" (John 3:16).

It is the will of God that everyone receive eternal salvation. The way to receive this salvation is to call upon the name of Jesus and confess Him as your Lord. The Bible says, "That if thou shalt confess with thy mouth the Lord Jesus, and shalt believe in thine heart that God hath raised him from the dead, thou shalt be saved. For whosoever shall call upon the name of the Lord shall be saved" (Romans 10:9,13).

Jesus has given salvation, healing, and countless benefits to all who call upon His name. These benefits can be yours if you receive Him into your heart by praying this prayer:

> *Heavenly Father, I come to You admitting that I am a sinner. Right now, I choose to turn away from sin, and I ask You to cleanse me of all unrighteousness. I believe that Your Son, Jesus, died on the cross to take away my sins. I also believe that He rose again from the dead so that I may be justified and made righteous through faith in Him. I call upon the name of Jesus Christ to be the Savior and Lord of my life. Jesus, I choose to follow You, and I ask that You fill me with the power of the Holy Spirit. I declare right now that I am a born again child of God. I am free from sin and full of the righteousness of God. I am saved in Jesus' name, amen.*

If you have just received Jesus Christ as your Savior or if this book has impacted your life, we would like to hear from you. Please write us at:

Mac Hammond Ministries
P.O. Box 29469
Minneapolis, Minnesota 55429-2946

You can also visit us on the web at
mac-hammond.org

About The Author

Lynne Hammond travels nationally and internationally as a teacher and author on the subject of prayer. She regularly writes articles in the *Winner's Way* magazine and publishes a newsletter called *PrayerNotes* for people of prayer. Her books include, *Heaven's Power for the Harvest, Staying Faith, When It's Time for a Miracle, Living in God's Presence,* and *Dare to Be Free.* In addition, Lynne's prayer books, *The Master Is Calling, Renewed in His Presence, Secrets to Powerful Prayer,* and *When Healing Doesn't Come Easily,* have been translated into several different languages.

Lynne and her husband, Mac, pastor Living Word Christian Center, a large and growing church in Minneapolis, Minnesota. The desire of Lynne's heart is to impart Holy Spirit and corporate-led prayer to churches throughout the world. Under her leadership, the prayer ministry at Living Word has become a nationally and internationally recognized model for developing effective pray-ers in the local church. Each week at Living Word, 88 prayer groups led by 85 prayer leaders assemble for the purpose of following the direction of the Spirit in prayer. This last year, more than 9,000 people participated in chapel prayer, which meets every morning at Living Word. Over 12,000 Internet subscribers receive the daily prayer summaries (known as the Global Prayer Alert Network) from these meetings.

Other Books Available From

MAC HAMMOND
M I N I S T R I E S

By Lynne Hammond

The Master Is Calling
Discovering the Wonders of Spirit-Led Prayer

When It's Time for a Miracle
The Hour of Impossible Breakthroughs Is Now!

Staying Faith
How to Stand Until the Answer Arrives

Heaven's Power for the Harvest
Be Part of God's End-Time Spiritual Outpouring

Living in God's Presence
Receive Joy, Peace, and Direction in the Secret Place of Prayer

Renewed in His Presence
Satisfying Your Hunger for God

When Healing Doesn't Come Easily

Secrets to Powerful Prayer
Discovering the Languages of the Heart

Dare to Be Free!

The Table of Blessing
Recipes From the Family and Friends of Living Word Christian Center

Other Books Available From

By Mac Hammond

Angels at Your Service
Releasing the Power of Heaven's Host

Doorways to Deception
How Deception Comes, How It Destroys, and How You Can Avoid It

Heirs Together
Solving the Mystery of a Satisfying Marriage

The Last Millennium
A Revealing Look at the Remarkable Days Ahead and How You Can
Live Them to the Fullest

Living Safely in a Dangerous World
Keys to Abiding in the Secret Place

Plugged In and Prospering
How to Find and Fill Your God-Ordained Place in the Local Church

Positioned for Promotion
How to Increase Your Influence and Capacity to Lead

Real Faith Never Fails
Detecting (and Correcting) Four Common Faith Mistakes

Simplifying Your Life
Divine Insights to Uncomplicated Living

The Way of the Winner
Running the Race to Victory

Water, Wind & Fire
Understanding the New Birth and the Baptism of the Holy Spirit

Water, Wind & Fire—The Next Steps
Developing Your New Relationship With God

Who God Is Not
Exploding the Myths About His Nature and His Ways

Other Books Available From

MAC HAMMOND
M I N I S T R I E S

BY MAC HAMMOND (CONTINUED)

Winning Your World
Becoming the Bold Soul Winner God Created You to Be

Winning In Your Finances
How to Walk God's Pathway to Prosperity

Yielded and Bold
How to Understand and Flow With the Move of God's Spirit

BY MAC AND LYNNE HAMMOND

Keys to Compatibility
Opening the Door to a Marvelous Marriage

*For more information or a complete catalog
of teaching CDs and other materials,
please write:*

Mac Hammond Ministries
P.O. Box 29469
Minneapolis, MN 55429–2946

Or visit us on the web at:

mac-hammond.org